*Wuji Qi Gong* is an excellent introduction to qi gong practice, gently taking the beginner through the fundamentals that apply to both static and moving styles. I like the way the authors root the practice in the discusson of the primordial elements and their novel explanation of the wisdom contained in the trigrams and hexagrams of the *Yi Jing*, the inter-penetration of Yin and Yang, and the subtleties of Chinese internal alchemy. ***Richard Bertschinger, Author, The Secret of Everlasting Life***

This scholarly book explores the metaphysical basis and practice of WuJiShi QiGong, a very deep and ancient path for longevity and spiritual develop-ment. Written for serious students, it hones in on the essential practice. Those who train with an accom-plished teacher will find it even more valuable. By making knowledge of WuJiShi QiGong accessible, Stephen Elliott brings a special gift to Western prac-titioners. This challenging and worthwhile form of practice is made available for those wishing to join mind, body, and spirit. ***Dr. Richard Brown, M.D.***

*Wuji Qi Gong* casts a whole new light on the prac-tice of standing meditation. The authors have done a tremendous job linking the fundamentals of the practice to the ancient concept of the primordial el-ements and the method to achieve self-transforma-tion and longevity. ***Jacques Bélanger, Tai Chi and Qi Gong Practitioner***

This ancient archetypal diagram is where the conscious mind, the subconscious mind, and the eternal laws of nature meet for reflection, understanding, and integration into daily life. As a teacher and practitioner of TCM, I encourage you to re-examine your practice in the light of these profound ideas about Fire and Water and their part in health and aging. *Carol Elliott, Licensed Acupuncturist*

As a practitioner it is a real pleasure to recommend this fine work. The authors have made what was previously hidden - visible, and what was previously complex - simple. From their bare bones easy to follow explanation of the ordering of the elemental hexagrams of the *Yi Jing* to the no nonsense "how to" of the stages of practice, they have managed to capture what others have only hinted at previously. Their elucidation of attentional focus, the real meaning of the "turning of the light around", and the need to keep breathing/relaxing... These gems alone will make this a beloved classic to be read, used, shared, discussed, and re-read around the globe for lifetimes to come. Bravo! *Stephen Michael Hawley, Personal Enrichment Programs*

Indeed, this method connects our inner circuitry to the omnipresent ever flowing qi, allowing it to do what it does – heal, protect, and empower. Without sacrifice, *Wuji Qi Gong* reveals and simplifies complicated ancient teachings in a way that is manageable for the 21st century Western mind. *Jenna Ritter, Founder, Dhara*

It is with great pleasure and some small measure of pride that I recommend this book, *Wuji Qi Gong,* by my former student and assistant instructor from *The Gompa Center*, Stephen Elliott. Mr. Elliott is a most erudite scholar of oriental mythology, science, history and Daoist longevity concepts. This volume is a testament to his ability to penetrate into the mysteries of Daoist esoteric knowledge in a way that few Westerners are capable of, while making these principles and concepts clear to the general public. Mr. Elliott's ability to break these difficult concepts down to understandable theories and exercises that make sense to the reader is nothing short of revolutionary and much needed in today's over stressed world. ***John P. Painter, Ph.D., ND, Director of The Gompa Center for Chinese and Tibetan Internal Martial Arts and Health Studies***

In *Wuji Qigong*, Elliott and Lin shine the light of deep understanding over the *Yi Jing* by translating its esoteric principles into a series of simple, integrated exercises that will rejuvenate the practitioner. I heartily recommend this book to anyone seeking a meditative "map" that leads to health and longevity. ***Master Robert Peng, Founder, Elixir Light Qigong***

I have found Wuji Qi Gong to be a very clear sustainable practice which leads to significant improvement in physical, emotional, and spiritual health. Elliott and Lin have correctly understood and described the approach to qi cultivation as articulated by the classics via the process of the reversal and intermingling of the elements. To be able to apprehend and share in a practical way the fruits of Eastern natural sciences is a significant accomplishment reflecting decades of effort and experimentation. *Wuji Qigong* additionally rests on the authors' substantial understanding of Western physiology and is positioned to contribute to any future dialogues on the scientific exploration of human potential. To reconcile the insights of the past with the terms of the future is to live most fully in the present. Like the ancient sages, the authors have indeed pointed the way. ***Brian McKenna, Doctor of Oriental Medicine, Licensed Acupuncturist***

The author's insights into the historical and philosophical basis of Wuji Qi Gong is truly profound. To my knowledge their explanation of the four primordial elements and the *Yi Jing* has never before been presented - at least not in the English lauguage. It has inspired me to delve deeper into my work with this meditation system. Thanks for sharing this gem.
***Andrew Stronski, Yoga and Martial Arts Colleague***

After many years of seeking the way to heightened understanding and awareness through the practice of yoga, martial arts, and Traditional Chinese Medicine, *Wuji Qi Gong* makes the ultimate goal seem attainable. It provides in depth explanation and easy to follow guidance to what is otherwise a *very complex* subject. Anyone dedicated to the journey of self-discovery will find it to be of great value. ***Kristin Turner, Yoga and Martial Arts Colleague***

# WUJI QI GONG

# AND THE SECRET OF
# IMMORTALITY

## Book 1

by
Stephen Elliott
with Dr. Meng-Sheng Lin

Swanstone

# Wuji Qi Gong

## And The Secret Of Immortality

by Stephen Elliott with Dr. Meng-Sheng Lin

ISBN 978-0-9786399-4-5

071013

Swanstone is an imprint of COHERENCE Press

Cover design by Stephen Elliott

Calligraphy by Dr. Meng-Sheng Lin

Photography by T.R.E.

Typesetting by COHERENCE Press

Published by
COHERENCE Press

email: inquiries@coherencepress.com

## ~ Author's Note ~

The material in this book is a synthesis of the authors' personal research and experience gained over several decades of study, practice, contemplation, and teaching.

Theories being put forward are those of the authors. When possible, they have been complemented by the work of others. Where Chinese texts are concerned, Dr. Meng-Sheng Lin has provided invaluable guidance in both translation and interpretation.

I would like to thank all of my teachers and students with special thanks to Sifu John Painter, and my sister, Carol Elliott, L.Ac., who've had even more to do with this work than they might know.

The text assumes some familiarity with the *Yi Jing - The Book of Changes,* possibly the most famous of all Chinese texts. It also assumes some knowledge of Chinese medicine and traditional Chinese martial arts. As the treatment of these topics is beyond the scope of this work, the reader is encouraged to refer to other sources for more information.

The practice of Wuji Qi Gong is a long term undertaking.....years not months. This being said, each day that you practice, you will feel different, more centered, more robust, faster, stronger, more alert, more aware....

It is imperative that the body be *relaxed* before undertaking the practice. By this we mean that the body should not be stiff or inflexible. One must have good command of one's own *relaxation response*, the ability to consciously "let go" of tension in the body and mind.

Both "flexibility" and "relaxation response" relate highly to one's breathing pattern which *must* be slow, deep, and rhythmic.

This is because Wuji Qi Gong, while very gentle, is physically, mentally, and energetically demanding. Over the course of practice, the body and mind go through many changes that require conscious guidance, specifically *relaxation*.

The practice is very potent. For this reason, it is recommended that you approach it very gradually, practicing no more than 5 minutes per day for the first month.

Then increase practice time very gradually up to a total of 20 minutes per day. Ideally, this is divided into two 10 minute periods, one in the morning and the second in the afternoon.

Please adhere to the instructions with care.

# ~ *Table of Contents* ~

If you can only,
breath by breath,
bring all into choice harmony,
you exchange this bundle
of sun-dried bones
for a clear-running
sweet-jade spring.[1]


Master Yu-Yan
circa 1284

# ~ *Preface* ~

We've chosen to call this book *Wuji Qi Gong*. Even though "qi gong" is a fairly recent term, its use arising only during the 20th century. We choose this name because, otherwise, people will not know what it is we're talking about.

However, the method being discussed is some portion of an esoteric practice that is thousands of years old. It is as least as old as the ancient Chinese character for "navel", 𡰪 , "pi", which is thought to date back to the Yellow Emperor (circa 2500 B.C.E.) or before.

Our belief is that the practice, in some form, co-incides with the recognition and exaltation of the four *primordial elements*, Air, Earth, Fire, and Water, which date back to China (5000 B.C.E.), India (3500 B.C.E.), Egypt (2500 B.C.E.), and Europe (1000 A.C.E). These time frames are educated estimates. Where the method actually originated and the path by which it spread is unknown.

In any case, traces of the essential method, though obscure, exist in the yogas of Taoism, Hinduism, and Kashmiri Shaivism, even today.

Volumes have been written about it in ancient China alone. However, as opposed to explaining how to do it, the prolific *Taoist* writings celebrate the experience without divulging the "secret", i.e. the essential method by which the experience may be *experienced.*

I've been a student of Eastern esoterica for several decades and have studied and practiced very hard. As of the mid-90s I had a pretty solid understanding of yoga, meditation, and martial arts, and I'd had my share of profound experiences. This includes "living" with kundalini shakti in all its glory for a decade.

However, my knowledge was incomplete and I knew it and I was always looking for the piece of the puzzle that I felt in my heart was missing.

I first learned of the *subtle practice* of Wuji Qi Gong proper in the book *Wujishi Breathing Exercise* (the author of which remains something of a mystery), which I discovered just a short time after its publication in the mid-90s.

When I received the book, I began poring over it right away, trying to determine if it contained anything novel, as I have bookshelves of this kind of material, all of which I'd combed through very carefully. And it did...

In particular, there are a number of *very specific* instructions that I'd not run across before. I can safely say that I'd been exposed to all of the principles earlier, via either direct yoga/martial arts instruction or by way of written material, but without this *degree of specificity.*

I began studying *the exercise* intensely, trying to make heads or tales of it. This was not particularly easy because the instructions contained in the book are articulated in a way that make them quite difficult to understand, and they are anatomically incorrect.

So, making sense of it was an experiential process of trial and error. However, I'd studied many of the classics thoroughly, and, because in my own practice I'd been fortunate enough to "touch it" numerous times, I had a pretty good idea what I was looking for.

Within a few months I was very confident that I was on the path of a very important personal discovery! Within a year, I knew I'd found what I'd been looking for since I began my study of yoga and martial arts 20 years earlier...*the essential meditative method that yields the profound experiences of legend!*

Stephen Elliott

February 2010, Year of the Tiger

## ~ *Introduction* ~

Within *this canon* lies a method that is extremely profound, a technique that has, over time, and for this reason, been intentionally veiled.

The method is that of *Wuji Qi Gong*.

Yoga, meditation, and martial arts counsel us to lift the head, sit and stand straight, relax, be still, quiet the mind, and breathe...

Regarding these points, there are as many approaches as there are systems or even teachers.

Where ancient knowledge is concerned, this is natural.

"Lifting the head", "sinking the qi to the dan tien", "lifting the hui yin", "breathing", "remaining still"...these things are common knowledge.

But the way in which we go about them is critical to the outcome. It is the difference in success and failure.

Wuji Qi Gong requires the body, mind, and breath to be coordinated in a *very precise* way. This sounds self-evident, but it isn't.

It is intricate, consisting of numerous steps or "facets" that are mutually dependent like pieces of a puzzle.

*The practice involves the union of the four primordial elements, Air, Earth, Fire, and Water.*

The elements are analogous to the four wheels of a car. With all four wheels, the car functions properly and we are able to go where we wish with speed and control.

But remove even one wheel and the car fails in its essential purpose – four wheels are necessary.

The essential "elements" of Wuji Qi Gong are similarly requisite for it to function.

By "function", we mean, for it to yield profound benefit for the practicer in terms of health, well-being, performance, spiritual experience, and longevity.

Any single element is necessary but in itself insufficient. Air, Earth, Fire, and Water, must function *simultaneously* for complete success.

Not only must they function simultaneously, but they must also function *very precisely*, again, just as the four wheels of a car must work in perfect unison.

On a scale of 1 to 10, simultaneity and precision are the difference between "1" and "10", failure vs. great success.

Outwardly, Wuji Qi Gong has no observable characteristics. It is all *internal*. In this regard, we may think of it as meditation.

Even to the trained eye, there is nothing to see. Without understanding what to do, it is impenetrable.

One may not understand the method in a lifetime. Here the authors have been fortunate to understand even this much.

The correct *way* of Wuji Qi Gong is neither simple or complex. It is in-between. Yet, after it is understood, in retrospect, it appears simple. This is a characteristic of things worth knowing.

This being said, practicing it is challenge enough.

## ~ *The Essential Philosophy* ~

Wuji Qi Gong is rooted in the great philosophy and mysticism of Taoism. The symbolism is that of the *Bagua* or "eight trigrams", and the *Taiji* diagram.

The vocabulary is *Heaven*, *Earth*, *Fire*, and *Water*, the four primordial elements. It is the only vernacular that we have for discussing this ancient method.

It is a language and symbology that is rife with multiple meanings, some "true" and many intentionally false. It seems that it was intended to be this way, i.e. delightful for the initiated and confounding for the novice.

Wu 無 means "to vanish", the character depicting a forest that has disappeared. Vanishing is an analogy for "de-manifesting".

Ji 極 means "utmost, extreme limit, zenith". The inner character, also "ji"亟 has the meaning "Man struggling for life against an obstacle". The obstacle is *difficulty breathing*.

Wuji 無極 Qi Gong is a method by which *manifestation* may be reversed. It involves resolution of the difficulty – *by learning to breathe in harmony with Heaven and Earth*.

The Bagua (Fu Xi Arrangement)

The earliest known arrangement of the Bagua (the 8 trigrams) is attributed to its legendary creator, Fu Xi, one of China's three emperor immortals, who is said to have lived approximately 7000 years ago.

Legend has it that Fu Xi derived the design from the back of a turtle that crawled from the banks of the Yellow River where he had gone to meditate on the meaning of life.

Fu Xi is also considered to be the father of Chinese characteriture, Huang Ti, the Yellow Emperor later systematizing it.

The Bagua is the central concept behind the *Yi Jing* or *Book of Changes*. It has many meanings and many secrets. It's been the subject of inquiry for thousands of years.

The Bagua is considered to be a model of the cosmos, describing the very process of "manifestation", the means by which Lao Tzu's "10,000 things" come into being.

As man is considered a microcosm of the macrocosm, it is equally applicable to understanding human affairs, hence its use in divination.

One of the mysteries contained in the Bagua is the *secret of alchemy*, the process by which ordinary "elements" interact to produce something extraordinary – *the elixir of immortality.*

It contains the formula for the method by which aging and decay can be slowed, stopped, or even reversed, preserving health, well-being, and the vitality of youth.

In the Fu Xi arrangement, Heaven, Earth, Fire and Water are in the *cardinal* positions. Wind, Lake, Mountain, and Thunder are in the *ordinal* positions.

In this book, we will tend to limit the discussion to the cardinal "gua" (trigrams), the four primordial elements, Heaven (Air), Earth, Fire, and Water.

Heaven

Earth

## The Vertical Points

Heaven and Earth are the "vertical points" of the Bagua. They are the most fundamental – the most *primordial*. Each is a "force" and an "element".

Heaven is the force "Yang" and the element "Air". Earth is the force "Yin" and the element "Earth".

Heaven is positive, upward, and pure Yang. It is symbolized by three solid lines. Earth is negative, downward, and pure Yin. It is symbolized by three broken lines.

Heaven and Earth are opposites, just as two poles of a great magnet. This is the meaning of "taiji" " 太極 " , "great extreme poles". "Ji" in tai-ji, is the same character as "ji" in wu-ji.

The Taiji Diagram Without Dynamism

Between Heaven and Earth exists a "field", very much like the magnetic field that exists between Earth's north and south poles.

This idea is symbolized by the "Taiji Diagram", Heaven being white and pure Yang, and Earth being black and pure Yin.

But as of yet, the diagram has no change or dynamism and the forces of Yin and Yang are more accurately depicted like this, which represents "differentiation" without "dynamism".

Heaven and Earth are *pure* Yang and *pure* Yin, and as such can only demonstrate their own *essential* natures. Heaven is Yang, Yang, Yang, and Earth is Yin, Yin, Yin, and that's it!

This is a gross simplification, but the point is that Heaven cannot be Yin and Earth cannot be Yang, even to the slightest degree!

Heaven and Earth are Yang and Yin. They set the "stage".[2] However, due to their purity they themselves are unable to play upon it. They need actors or "agents" to do their bidding in the world.

The first order agents of Heaven and Earth are Fire and Water, which Heaven and Earth *produce* through their union.

Heaven Combines With Earth to Produce Fire

Earth Combines With Heaven to Produce Water

Fire inherits it top and bottom lines from Heaven and its middle line from Earth. Conversely, Water inherits its top and bottom lines from Earth and its middle line from Heaven.

In this way, Fire and Water are the "offspring" of Heaven and Earth. Fire is 2/3 Heaven and 1/3 Earth. Water is 2/3 Earth and 1/3 Heaven.

The two beget the four.

Fire

 Water

## The Horizontal Points

Fire and Water are the "horizontal points" of the Bagua. Like Heaven and Earth, they are exact opposites. However, they are "impure", each being part Yin and part Yang. Their impurity gives them the ability to move, adapt, change, and effect. It endows them with dynamism...*life*.

Fire's essential action is that of converting Earth (matter with substance) into Heaven (nothing – gas). In this way Fire is Heaven's emissary between Earth and Heaven.

Water's essential action is that of converting Heaven (nothing) into Earth (matter with substance). Water is Earth's emissary between Heaven and Earth.

Fire and Water are mutually destructive. If Fire "outweighs" Water, Fire will destroy Water. If Water outweighs Fire, Water will destroy Fire. If they are combined in equal measures they will destroy each other.

A single drop of water extinguishes the flame of a single candle – both Fire and Water *disappear*.

Heaven

Fire

Water

Earth

The Cardinal Gua

Together, Heaven, Earth, Fire, and Water are the four cardinal gua of the Bagua. They are the primordial elements, Air, Earth, Fire, and Water.

Heaven and Earth are forces and elements. Fire and Water are their dynamic agents.

Via the union of Heaven and Fire, Earth and Fire, Heaven and Water, Earth and Water, the ordinal gua, Thunder, Mountain, Wind, and Lake come into being, yielding the 8 (ba) trigrams (gua).

The union of the 8 gua with each other gives rise to the 64 hexagrams of the *Yi Jing*, the union of the 64 giving rise to Lao Tzu's "10,000 things".

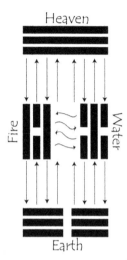

Fire & Water Reacting In The Field
of Heaven & Earth

When brought into *cautious proximity* in the field of Heaven and Earth, Fire and Water "react".

Fire and Water are dependent on Heaven and Earth – *without the field of Heaven and Earth, Fire and Water do not exist.* For the reaction to occur, both conditions, the *field* and the *proximity* must be true.

Fire and Water are mutually destructive, but via cautious proximity, synergy and harmony may be brought about between them, yielding a relationship that *governs, protects, and produces vs. destroys.*

The Taiji Diagram Demonstrating Both
Force and Dynamism

Fire and Water, when added to Heaven and Earth, give the Taiji Diagram "dynamism", Yang taking on the shape of a leaping flame rising on the left and Yin taking on the shape of a drop of water falling on the right.

It may also be seen as the active interplay between the primordial Dragon and Tiger.

The diagram appears to be turning in the clockwise direction, Yin falling on the right side and Yang rising on the left side.

You might ask, in this depiction, where are the elements Fire and Water? The answer is that they remain hidden in their respective camps.

Fire is 2/3 Yang and remains hidden in the white of Yang, Water is 2/3 Yin and remains hidden in the black of Yin.

## ~ *The Earthly Order* ~

The Taiji diagram at the left corresponds to the clockwise order of the cardinal gua, Heaven–Water–Earth representing the Yin phase, and Earth–Fire–Heaven representing the Yang phase.

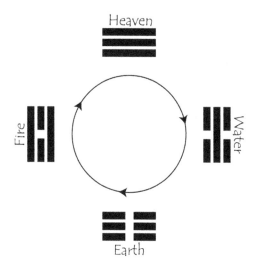

The Earthly Order
(Cardinal Gua In Clockwise Direction)

We will refer to this clockwise sequence as the "*Earthly* Order". It's the way of the Earthly world and the way we experience it. It is by definition, *changing*...

The Earthly Order is the "reality" that we tend to accept as being true and final.

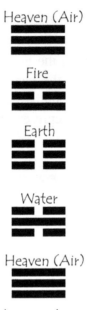

The Elemental Process

To understand the Earthly Order let's place it in a vertical continuum that we will refer to as the *elemental process*.

Starting with Heaven, from the bottom up, the trigrams are Heaven, Water, Earth, Fire, Heaven.

We see that Heaven is below Water, Water is below Earth, Earth is below Fire, and coming full circle, Fire is below Heaven.

In the parlance of the *Yi Jing*, Water is over Heaven, Earth is over Water, Fire is over Earth, and Heaven is over Fire. We'll come back to this.

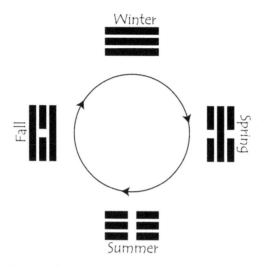

The Earthly Order Describes The Seasons

The Earthly Order describes the annual changing of seasons. In a clockwise direction, Spring is the season of Water, Summer is the season of Earth, Fall is the season of Fire, and Winter is the season of Heaven.

For annuals, Spring is the season of germination, Summer is the season of growth, Fall is the season of drying, and Winter is the season of decay and "de-manifestation", Yang returning to Heaven and Yin returning to Earth.

In the Spring perennials bud, in the Summer they leaf, in the Fall they shed, and in the Winter they stand bare.

29

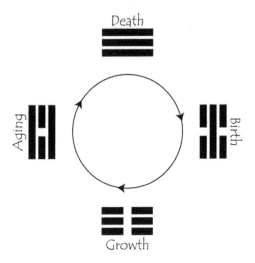

The Earthly Order & The Life Cycle Of Man

A central tenet of Taoism is that man is a microcosm of the macrocosm, and here we see that the Earthly Order also applies to *the changing seasons of man.*

Water is the season of birth, Earth is the season of growth and maturation, Fire is the season of aging, and Heaven is the season of death.

The Yin phase, Heaven–Water–Earth, is constructive. It promotes life and growth. Birth is a time of Air and Water.

During the season of Earth, the body grows by assimilating Earth. The process of growth is supported by Water from below, just as plants are supported by Water from below via their roots.

The Yang phase, Earth–Fire–Heaven, is destructive. It promotes aging, decay, and death.

Aging is a process of "inflammation", Fire gradually taking back the Water that Heaven provided. Fire is supported by Earth, Earth providing the fuel that feeds Fire.

When Water is exhausted, Fire finishes its task of sending us back to Heaven, Yang consuming and then leaving the body, Yin returning to Earth.

During the Yin phase, Water outweighs and vanquishes Fire. During maturation, Fire is becoming established in the body.

As we age, Fire begins to vanquish Water. In the end, Fire is victorious over Water and death and de-manifestation ultimately come...

~

Through the union of the 8 trigrams, the 64 "hexagrams" of the *Yi Jing* arise. A *hex*agram consists of 6 lines vs. three.

The 64 hexagrams represent every possible combination of the 8 trigrams, 8 squared being 64.

The hexagram Heaven over Fire is "The Same Purpose".

Heaven (Air)

The inner hexagram is Heaven over Wind, "Joining" (for the purpose of reproduction).

Fire

The hexagram Fire over Earth is "Advancing".

The hexagram Earth over Water is "Collective Force".

Earth

The inner hexagram is Water over Mountain, "Uneven, Limping".

The inner hexagram, Earth over Thunder, is "Reborn".

Water

The hexagram Water over Heaven is "Measured Waiting".

Heaven (Air)

The inner hexagram is Fire over Lake, "Separation".

The Yi Jing Speaks To The Elemental Process

The significance of the elemental arrangement is made clear by the *Yi Jing*, where we see the meaning of the "hexagrams" from bottom up, "Measured Waiting", "Collective Force", "Advancing", and "The Same Purpose". (See Appendix.)

*Measured Waiting* refers to germination or gestation. *Collective Force* refers to the rebirth of the masses. *Advancing* refers to the progression of age. *The Same Purpose* refers to the commonly shared destiny of death and the *re*union with Heaven.

The inner hexagrams in the same order are "Separation", "Returning", "Uneven", and "Coming To Meet".

*Separation* refers to separating from Heaven at birth. *Returning* refers to another cycle of life. *Uneven* refers to the crippling of age, and *Coming to Meet* refers specifically to (re)joining with Heaven for the purpose of being reborn.

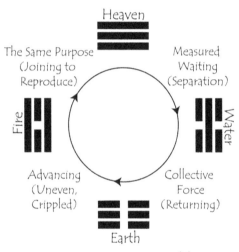

Yi Jing's Meaning – Earthly Order

If we place the meaning of the hexagrams in the *Earthly Order*, we can see that the *Yi Jing* clearly alludes to the cyclic process of reincarnation. Heaven, Water, Earth, Fire, Heaven, the inevitable wheel of life, *the way of things in the kingdom of Heaven and Earth it would seem....*

## ~ *The Heavenly Order* ~

Is the Earthly Order and its "wheel of life" immutable? Can one escape the inevitable clutches of aging, decay, and death? Is it possible to live forever?

China's ancient scientist/philosophers, e.g. Lao Tzu, Fu Xi, Shen Nung, Huang Ti, and others, were obsessed with this question.

It is generally accepted that the life span of pre-modern man (before 1800 A.C.E.) was no more than a few decades, this being due to war, pestilence, and disease. How generally true this was of the ancient East, we cannot know for sure.

(Fact: The decline of physical capacity, in virtually every dimension, begins at age 20. If age 20 marks the center, six o'clock relative to the Earthly Order, then life might have been expected to end at age 40.)

In any case, then, as today, the knowledge by which one might live long and well were of great value, not to mention that this knowledge was highly prized and sought after by the Emperors themselves!

Huang Ti, The Yellow Emperor, suggests that the ideal age to which man can aspire is 100 years, *the whole time remaining strong and vital.*

He says: "Those who have true wisdom remain strong, while those who have no wisdom grow old and feeble." [5] The wisdom to which Huang Ti refers is the means by which one *aligns with the way of Heaven.*

~

The Yin phase of the Earthly Order promotes life. The Yang phase that takes life away.

The question is then: Can the Yang phase be altered such that instead of decay and death, it promotes sustenance and life?

The ancients reasoned that the process that supports and maintains life must be a process wherein Water is protected from Fire.

As Fire and Water are mutually destructive, it must also in some way provide for the protection of Fire from Water.

Lastly, the process must be generative and constructive like the Yin phase vs. degenerative and destructive like the Yang phase.

How can a process like this be realized? Surprisingly, the answer to this profound metaphysical question was found to lie in the simple *technology* of the hearth!

The Earthen Cooking Vessel

The cooking vessel of old was an Earthen pot. In it one placed herbs (Earth, e.g. grains, vegetables, meat, plants, etc.) and Water, and below it – Fire.

Even though metals were in use in East Asia as long ago as 5000 B.C., the use of "earthen ware" for cooking has continued to this day.

In China, it is particularly favored for cooking *medicinal foods*. (In the traditional Chinese medical view, all foods are medicinal!)

This preference is supported by the understanding that Earth contains *elements* that combine with the herbs during the cooking process to produce the desired nutritional and curative effects.

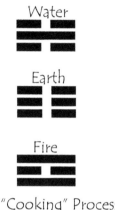

Water

Earth

Fire

## The "Cooking" Process

The Earthen "cauldron" maintains *cautious proximity* between Fire below and Water above, allowing Fire and Water to interact productively, warming the Water and cooking the herbs, both products providing sustenance.

The Earth of the cauldron protects the Water from the Fire and the Fire from the Water. At the same time, the Water protects the cauldron from overheating and being destroyed by Fire.

Fire warms Earth from below, Earth governs Fire. Earth warms Water, Water protects Earth from above. Each helps and protects the next. Earth mediates and sustains the interaction.

In the greater scheme of things, Heaven (Air) feeds and sustains the Fire. The heated Water sending Water, Air, (and Wind), back to Heaven.

Heaven

Water

Earth

Fire

Heaven

The "Alchemical" Process

In this process, Heaven, Earth, Fire, and Water produce something special, something that sustains life and promotes growth, *warmth, food,* and the third outcome, *Wind.*

In this light, the kitchen is no less wondrous now than then! Let's examine the order of the elements that realize this *alchemical process.*

Heaven (Air) is below Fire, fanning and nourishing Fire. Fire is below Earth, Earth mediating its interaction with Water. Earth is below Water, containing and protecting it from Fire.

Water is below Heaven (Air), the steam produced, a combination of Air, Water, (and Wind), returning to Heaven, thus completing the alchemical process.

Does this order look familiar?

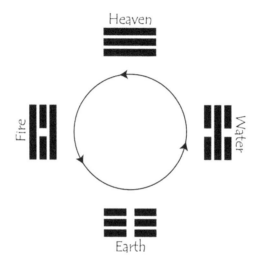

The Heavenly Order
(Cardinal Gua In A Counter-Clockwise Direction)

Let's look again at the cardinal gua, this time in a counterclockwise sequence, Heaven, Fire, Earth, Water, Heaven, etc. We will refer to this progression as the "Heavenly Order".

We find that the Heavenly Order and its *alchemical process* is simply the opposite of the Earthly Order and its *elemental process*!

In the context of the hearth, the Heavenly Order sustains, protects, and produces. Can the life of man be so benefitted? If so, how?

As the seasons of man advance according to the Earthly Order, can their progression be slowed or reversed?

The secret is in the progression of time...

If we place the Fu Xi Bagua and its Earthly Order in front of a mirror, the reflection transforms it into the Heavenly Order. Hence, the mystery of the "Bagua mirror".

Time In Reverse

Similarly, if we place a clock in front of a mirror, what do we see...*time* running in reverse.

Is the Heavenly Order then, that to be aspired to by man in his quest for immortality?

To answer this question, the ancients went on to model the human in terms of the elements, trying to understand his/her correspondences.

They determined the four elements in the human body to be arranged in this way....

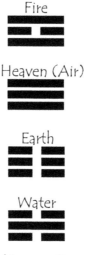

Fire

Heaven (Air)

Earth

Water

The Human Process

Water exists in a pool at the base of the torso. Anatomically this pool refers to the bladder. Alchemically, it refers to a pool of essence –"jin".

Above that is the element Earth and the organs that support Earth's assimilation, the stomach and intestines.

Above Earth is Heaven (Air), and the respiratory anatomy that supports Air, the airways, lungs, and thoracic cavity.

Fire is the etherial Mind, the *light* of consciousness. Fire resides in the head.

The "human process", they determined, is similar to the elemental process, and no less problematic relative to longevity. Water is below Earth, Fire is above Earth with Air between.

Like the elemental process, Water exists below (Earth) nourishing Earth from below yet failing to protect it from above.

Fire exists above Earth and is fanned by Heaven (Air). Fire is not well regulated (just as the mind tends not to be well regulated).

Heaven, Earth, Fire, and Water do not interact productively for the good of all....

Like in nature, in man the elements exist in a "non-sustainable" arrangement, one that ultimately leads to dysfunction, aging, decay, and death.

Can the human process, they wondered, be brought into alignment with the well *regulated* alchemical process of nourishment and life?

If so, it must involve changing the human process to be like that of Heaven, in effect "reordering" the elements in man to bring the process into harmony and prosperity.

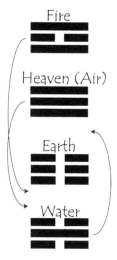

Reordering The Elements Of Man

To achieve this, Heaven (Air) would be placed below Fire, Fire would be placed below Earth, Earth would be placed below Water, and Water would be placed below Heaven.

In this configuration, the elements may then work in harmony and synergy to produce something special, something nourishing, something that sustains life – *the elixir of immortality*.

Heaven

Water

Earth

Fire

Heaven

The Human Alchemical Process

Once reordered, the process is identical to that of the hearth. Let's examine the outcomes in the context of the human body.

*Heaven is below Fire:* Heaven is also the element "Air". Air fans Fire, much as a blacksmith's bellows. Vitality in the human body relates directly to the quality of Fire, where the goal is a hot fire that burns brightly but is well regulated. In the body, Air is breath. *To effect the alchemy, Air is "lowered" to fan Fire.*

*Fire is below Earth:* Fire is the mind. It is the active Yang agent – the motive force in the alchemical process. *To effect the alchemy, Fire must be lowered, placing it beneath Earth.*

*Earth is below Water:* Earth contains Water and protects Water from Fire, Earth also protecting Fire from Water. In the alchemical process, Earth is relatively stable but must be *allowed* to sink. *To effect the alchemy, we let go to the force of Earth – gravity, allowing Earth to settle down.*

*Water is below Heaven:* Water is the Yin agent in the alchemical process. Water cools and protects Earth from the intense heat of Fire. The minerals of which Earth exists, intermingle with the water and are considered a subtle ingredient in the alchemical process. *To effect the alchemy, Water is raised to meet with Earth.*

*Water supports Heaven:* Water produces steam (a form of Wind), containing both Water and Air, thereby returning Water to Heaven, from whence it came originally. Steam is Heaven's reward for fanning fire.

(Fact: With the creation of steam comes a motive force of immense power. In the gaseous state water occupies 1600 times the volume as in its liquid state. Hence, the incredible force that is unleashed when water boils.)

In the body, steam is "qi". In modern parlance, it is "bioenergy". It is the *motive force* in the body, very much as we understand steam to be the motive force in a steam engine. When the body produces qi effectively and efficiently, vitality results.

Once produced, qi fills the container in which it is generated, pushing itself through the channels of the body, very much as steam produced by a boiler pushes its way through a system of pipes to distribute heat or pressure.

~

We see that the human "alchemical process" yields a very different outcome from the elemental process. Like the alchemy of the hearth, every interaction realizes mutual benefit.

Once again, the *Yi Jing* speaks to the alchemical process, but even more clearly than it describes the elemental process, where we see the meaning of the "hexagrams" from bottom up: "Great Possession", "Clarity", "Union" and "Resolution". (Again, refer to the Appendix for this discussion.)

*Great Possession* refers to the vitality that comes from the union of Heaven (Air) with Fire. *Clarity* and *Insight* refers to the understanding gained via the bringing together of Fire beneath Earth.

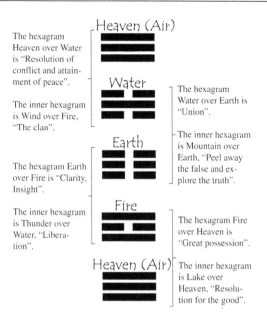

The hexagram Heaven over Water is "Resolution of conflict and attainment of peace".

The inner hexagram is Wind over Fire, "The clan".

The hexagram Earth over Fire is "Clarity, Insight".

The inner hexagram is Thunder over Water, "Liberation".

The hexagram Water over Earth is "Union".

The inner hexagram is Mountain over Earth, "Peel away the false and explore the truth".

The hexagram Fire over Heaven is "Great possession".

The inner hexagram is Lake over Heaven, "Resolution for the good".

Heaven (Air)

Water

Earth

Fire

Heaven (Air)

## The Yi Jing Speaks To The Alchemical Process

*Union* refers to joining with Tao that is realized by the uniting of Water above Earth. *Resolution of conflict and the attainment of peace* refers to an ending the circle of birth, life, death, birth, via the amalgamation of Water with Heaven.

The inner hexagrams in the same order are "Resolution for the good", "Liberation", "Peeling away the false to see the truth", and "The clan".

*Resolution for the good* refers to the decision to pursue the quest for life via the accumulation of "life force" (qi) via breathing. *Liberation* refers

47

to stepping off the wheel of life by placing Fire below Earth (vs. above).

*Peeling away the false to see the truth* refers to the realization that comes by elevating Water. *The clan* refers to entering the fellowship of the immortals.

Once again, if we place the meaning of the hexagrams in the cyclic context of the Heavenly Order we can see things a bit more completely.

The *Yi Jing* intimates that there is something very special about the Heavenly Order, something "liberating", the obvious meaning being the ending the perpetual cycle of birth, life, death – "joining the immortals".

The means by which this is accomplished is that of "reversing". *The Secret of the Golden Flower* another Taoist classic says, "The whole work of turning the light around uses the method of reversal." [4]

Here "turning the light around" has multiple meanings. One of the meanings is "reflecting one's own light upon one's self".

The other meaning is consciously following *The Way Of Heaven* vs. unconsciously going along with *The Way Of Earth*, its opposite...

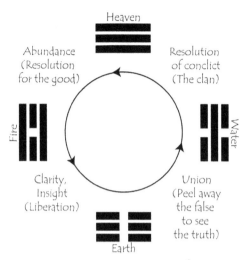

## Yi Jing's Meaning - Heavenly Order

Wuji Qi Gong is some portion of the method by which this is accomplished. It is a practice that facilitates the "reordering" of the elements in man, so man can aspire to *The Way Of Heaven*.

In so doing, it *reverses* the process of manifestation, i.e. birth, maturation, aging, and death, thereby returning to the vitality, resiliency, and softness of infancy. Hence, the Taoist notion of "prenatal qi".

Prenatal qi is that with which we are born. It is consumed as we age like the wax of a candle. Prenatal qi is generated and renewed via the Heavenly Order and its *alchemical process*. The grail in which this qi of life is formed is the center.

The Taiji Diagram Depicting Alchemy

"Alchemy" is the meaning of the Taiji diagram as we know it. The white and black dots indicate *the lowering of Fire and the raising of Water in the field of Heaven and Earth.*

Via the Heavenly Order and its alchemical process, the elements unite to protect, generate, and produce, vs. destroy.

Each element interacts with the next in a synergistic and transformative manner *producing* something new and extraordinary – "Qi", 氣.

Qi is the basic ingredient in Taoist alchemy, successive stages involving building, circulating, refining, etc.

With refinement, qi separates into essence and spirit, the three forming the principal energies in the body: jin, qi, and shen (essence, energy, and spirit).

## ~ *Wuji* ~

The Earthen cauldron is the intermediary between Fire and Water, which if brought into direct contact will subdue each other.

Earth serves to contain Water and temper Fire. In the *Can Tong Qi*, it is said that Earth combines with Fire and Water to produce *the elixir of immortality*.

In reality, the reaction occurs in the cauldron of the body. The cauldron is the body, and the body is of Earth. However, the cauldron does not "function" unless both Heaven and Earth are properly established.

Heaven and Earth generate the field. Air, Earth, Fire, and Water are the ingredients. Their reaction occurs at the Spirit Gate, the Qi Union, the Life Stem, Ren 8, the center, the point of origin of the body, "pi" 閪 , "the navel which is supposed to be in communication with the head through channels in which circulate the - 氣 vital spirits."[5] (The modern character "pi" is 毘.)

The navel is the pathway to the energetic middle of the body, the "sea of qi", "dan tien", or *elixir field*, which fills with qi. With practice the entire body becomes a vast flowing river of qi connecting with *Tao*.

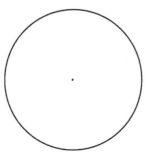

The Wuji Diagram

"Wuji", 無極, most often translated as "void", "nothing", or "nothingness", means *before differentiation* where differentiation is the process by which matter comes into existence.

The "Wuji Diagram" is frequently depicted as an empty white circle. It is rarely depicted with its more complete meaning as a white circle with a "point".

This "point" is "the center". It is the gateway to "Wuji" – "prior to manifestation". It is the means by which we come to know *Tao*. Oddly, though perhaps only by happenstance, the character "wu" 無 , resembles a gate lit from behind.

Wuji is the center of the Bagua. Here the forces of Heaven and Earth meet with the four primordial elements. Lao Tzu's "10,000 things" emerge from Wuji like matter from a theoretical *white hole*.

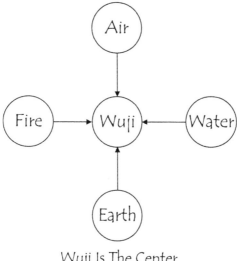

Wuji Is The Center

If we look inside the character "ji" 極 , we find the simpler inner character, also "ji" 亟 "A man who acts, who struggles, with his mouth and with his hand, between Heaven and Earth, to gain his *point*".[6] (See Appendix.)

Buddha said, "Place the mind on one *point*, and everything can be done."[7] The *one point* is the navel, the point of origin of the body. It is the crucible where the "reaction" occurs.

Just as the umbilical connects us to our mother before birth, the navel, "Ming Di", or "life stem" is the primary *celestial stem*, that connects us with *Tao*.

## ~ *Wuji Qi Gong - The Practice* ~

Yin is the foundation of the body. Yin fuel's the Fire of Yang. When Yin is exhausted Yang is extinguished.

In concept, it is much like a candle. Yin is the wax. Yang is the flame. When the wax is gone, the flame dies.

Human life is much like this. As we age, our candle grows shorter, Yin being consumed by Yang – Water by Fire.

Therefore, if we are to sustain life we must add wax back to the candle, continuously.

If we add a little, our health is improved. If we add more, our lives are lengthened. If we add even more, the process of aging is reversed.

Wuji Qi Gong is the means by which we add Yin. With the added Yin, Yang is also supported in greater measure. This is the purpose of Wuji Qi Gong.

Like the process of cooking, it is "technology", invented by man, but bestowed by Tao, for the purpose of extending life and circumventing the endless cycle of death and rebirth.

It involves aspiring to The Way of Heaven, thereby circumventing The Way of Earth. Along the way, it improves health, increases performance, and lengthens life.

~

The practice should be approached with patience. One cannot learn how to do it overnight.

Nor can one progress in the practice with great haste. Each stage takes time. Being in a hurry only defeats progress.

Too little practice fails to take advantage of the precious time that we are given. Too much practice harms progress.

Every aspect of Wuji Qi Gong involves *the middle way*. If we are ever in doubt we can return to the middle way. It is ultimately correct, in every regard.

The longer we engage in the practice, the more potent its effects, i.e., it is more potent after twelve months of practice than it is after three.

At the outset, it is recommended that we practice no more than 5 minutes per day for the first month.

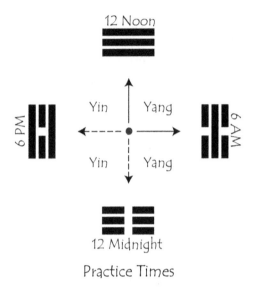

12 Noon

6 PM

Yin | Yang

Yin | Yang

6 AM

12 Midnight

Practice Times

With feelings of success, one is motivated to increase practice time. When this time comes, increase your practice time to 10 minutes per day.

With further confidence, increase practice time to 10 minutes *twice* per day. At this stage, we want to begin aligning our practice times with the time of the cardinal gua.

Ideal practice times are 6 A.M. and 6 P.M.; 12 noon and 12 midnight. In the parlance, these times are referred to as the ideal "firing times".

If 6 A.M. and 6 P.M. are not practical, the important thing is to *balance* practice times, practicing at the same time in the afternoon or evening as we do in the morning. However, because the exercise is also stimulating, it is best not too practice too close to bed time.

The longer we practice, i.e. months, years, decades, the more potent the effect, requiring less time to achieve the same intensity.

As the intensity increases, greater gains are made toward the goal of turning back the clock and preserving health.

### *Wuji Qi Gong is a 5 part practice:*

Part 1 is *Man United With Heaven and Earth*,
Part 2 is *The Practice of Air*
Part 3 is *The Practice of Fire*
Part 4 is *The Practice of Earth*, and
Part 5 is *The Practice of Water*

Each part should be learned at its own pace, being sure not to rush things, the next part being built on the foundation of the preceding part.

After all 5 parts have been learned and integrated, the goal is to carry the practice with us throughout the day, devoting a small portion of our consciousness to it at all times.

This being said, *be very conservative in The Practice of Water.* It adds tension.

## ~ Man United With Heaven And Earth ~

The Yellow Emperor says "From the earliest times the communication with Heaven has been the very foundation of life; this foundation exists between Yin and Yang and between Heaven and Earth and within the six points." [8] It is further explained that the "six points" are the 4 points of the compass, the Zenith, and the Nadir.

The practice of Wuji begins with the establishment of Heaven and Earth. Master Yu Yan says....

"The single human body is modeled on Heaven and cast in the form of Earth; it unites together Yin and Yang with Heaven and Earth. If man understands how this body unites together Yin and Yang with Heaven and Earth, he can partake in any discussion on the method of the restored Elixir!" [9]

Heaven is a positive *force* acting upon the body. It causes the head to rise up, the top of the head (Bai Hui, 100 Convergences, Du #20) *reaching* gently upward.

Earth is a negative *force*. It causes the base of the torso (the Hui Yin, Convergence of Yin, Ren 1) to sink down, *reaching* gently downward. This gentle reaching creates a separating force in the body, the head reaching upward, and the base of

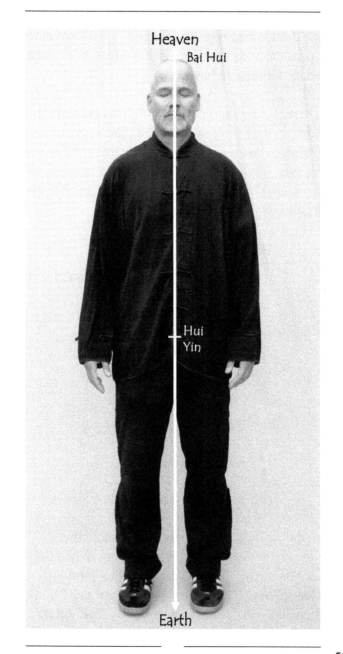

Heaven

Bai Hui

Hui
Yin

Earth

the torso reaching downward. This separation opens the Ming Men, the gate of life, the 4th point on the Governing Vessel (Du 4).

There is a gradual tightening, as though the body is the string of a Gu Qin, the very ancient Chinese stringed instrument, strung between Heaven and Earth. (The Qu Qin is said to have also been created by Immortal Fu Xi, the legendary creator of the Bagua!)

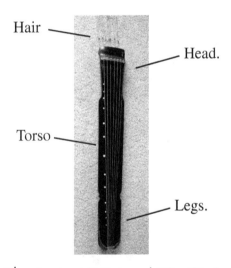

The Ancient 7 Stringed "Qu Qin"
(Courtesy Luc Jiang)

If the strings are too tight they will break. If they are too loose, they will not play. When they are just right, they vibrate with the harmony of Heaven and Earth. The "strings" are the Chong meridian, in Hindi they are the "Sushumna".

### *Step 1: Man United With Heaven And Earth*

*Man United With Heaven and Earth* requires very precise posture and subtle alignment of the entire body. It is accomplished in this way:

1. Stand with legs perfectly plumb and feet pointing straight ahead. The knees are straight but not locked. Gently press down with the feet.

2. The weight is naturally centered over the ankles, not too far forward or backward.

3. Allow the arms to hang by the sides in a natural way, trapezius and shoulders relaxed.

4. Begin lifting the topmost point of the head until the hands tingle. The posture accentuates a perfectly vertical straight line in the body connecting the Bai Hui and Hui Yin points. (See p77.)

5. Breathe slowly and deeply, six seconds in and six seconds out, through the nose.

6. Relax the tongue, allowing the tip to rest *very gently* against the roof of the mouth just above the two front teeth.

This is the point Yin Jiao, Gum Intersection, Du 28, the upper end of the Du meridian. When it touches, there is an electrical sensation.

7. Close your eyes and relax.

8. Keeping the mind focused on the exacting posture, reflect on the entirety of the body all at once. Feel your whole skin all at once. Maintain this focus.

9. Otherwise, remain perfectly still and breathe.

### *Discussion:*

*Man United With Heaven And Earth* is the essential posture of yoga, meditation, and martial arts, be it seated, standing, lying down, or moving.

Work with the instructions until you find the moment where the tingling in the hands and fingers is maximized. This tingling is "feedback" that the posture is optimal. It will eventually pervade the entire body.

In traditional Chinese medical terms, the tingling is a function of opening Ming Men, or Life Gate (Governing Vessel point 4), allowing the current of Heaven and Earth to flow through the body as if we are connected between the *supreme poles* of a battery.

Once you find the subtle moment, practice staying with it for 1, 2, 3, 5, 10, minutes at a time. Practice acquiring it when standing, walking, sitting, and lying down. Become extremely familiar with it.

There is no need for other postural adjustments or concerns. These things will take care of themselves.

Our goal is to train this posture so we are able to keep this "moment" 24 hours a day, even when we are walking, talking, moving about, and sleeping.

Practice this thoroughly. Until Heaven and Earth are properly established, you cannot proceed. Successive steps simply don't work.

During this practice our goal is to focus 100 per cent of our mental energy on our body. This, as opposed to allowing our mental energy to chase after thoughts. This is difficult but do not strain.

In the parlance, reflecting upon one's own body is referred to as "turning the light around", referring to the "light of consciousness".

*The Secret of the Golden Flower* says, "When we turn the light around, all of the energies in the body rise up".[10]

Our mental energy is highly potent and is ultimately the motive force for internal alchemy. It is "Fire".

# ~ Air ~

Heaven is the force Yang and the element Air. In the Chinese language, Air and "qi" employ the same character, 氣.

The reason that the old language makes no distinction between them is that there was no distinction. They were literally considered one and the same.

Air is the "life force of Heaven" drawn into the body from outside. Once it is in the body, it is still "life force". This life force is 氣 ,"qi". Cut off the supply and life ends – quickly.

A general idea is that more life force is better than less. A second belief is that life force can be accumulated, hence the potential to have more.

Qi is accumulated by drawing it in and storing it in the body, in the Qi Hai – the sea of qi – the sea of breath – the sea of life force. They are one and the same.

Fire also requires a steady supply of life force – Air. The more it gets the hotter and brighter it burns. Without it, Fire smoulders and dies.

As Fire is the impetus for the generation of qi in the body, qi is dependent on Air.

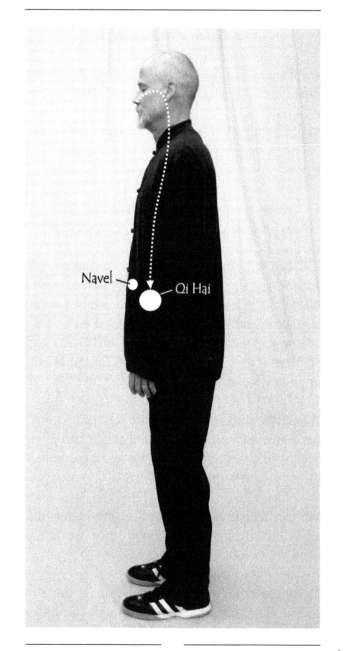

Navel

Qi Hai

## *Step 2: The Practice Of Air*

*The Practice of Air* involves *lowering* Air to fan Fire, i.e. sinking the breath to the Qi Hai.

Maintaining all of the conditions set forth in the instructions for *Man United With Heaven and Earth*:

1. Breathe slowly and deeply. Inhale for 6 seconds, exhale for 6 seconds. Relax during exhalation.

2. Develop the sense that upon inhalation, we are moving the breath *very gently* down, down, down, in the body until it reaches just below the level of the navel, Qi Hai, Sea of Qi, Ren 6. This anatomical area is also known as the "Dan Tien" or *Elixir Field*. There is no need for the breath to go any lower.

When the breath reaches the Qi Hai it will become apparent. It feels like a single "drop" of qi has fallen into the Sea of Qi and we can feel the ripples throughout the body.

We can feel it at the Qi Hai, in the hands, the legs, and throughout the body once we know what we're looking for.

3. At the completion of inhalation, begin exhaling smoothly and gently through the nose,

allowing the breath to rise back up of its own accord. Pay close attention to "letting go" of tension *inside* the body during exhalation.

## *Discussion:*

Keep the *Man United With Heaven and Earth* posture. Do not concern yourself with abdominal breathing or any manipulation of the muscles of respiration.

The posture, timing, and lowering of the breath facilitate proper involvement of the appropriate muscle groups. All we have to do is breathe at the approximate frequency of six seconds in and six seconds out, and relax during exhalation.

Lowering of the breath during inhalation, while maintaining *Man United With Heaven And Earth*, causes all of the muscles in the body to tense slightly.

For this reason, we must be particularly mindful of relaxing during exhalation. However, we must relax without losing the posture. Also, except for breathing, we must remain perfectly still.

The reason we use the breathing frequency of six seconds in and six seconds out (5 breaths per minute) is that it "pumps" the air, the blood, and the energy in the body. This pumping is an important aspect of the therapeutic and developmental affect.

Relaxation happens automatically under autonomic nervous system control when we are breathing slowly, deeply, and rhythmically.

When we stand for 5–10 minutes or more, it becomes stressful. As the body becomes stressed, low threshold muscle motor units, the small short but very strong muscles along the spine and throughout the body, tend to tighten.

As muscles tighten, both blood vessels and meridians, the channels that transport qi, constrict. This constriction defeats the process of "cultivating qi". For the practice to continue, *internal* tension must be managed.

However, if we are not breathing slowly, deeply, and rhythmically, the tension will not abate, no matter how hard we "try". Therefore, if we want to practice Wuji Qi Gong, breathing slowly, deeply, and rhythmically is imperative.

It takes time and practice to develop the ability to lower the breath comfortably. Some of this has to do with building the strength, endurance, and coordination of the diaphragm.

In time it will become completely natural.

## ~ *Fire* ~

Once Air has been established we begin the practice of Fire. Fire is the dynamic "agent" of Heaven. In man, Fire is the mind. To effect the alchemy, we must place Fire below Earth.

How are we to go about this? By placing the mind at the center, Ren 8, the navel.

What does this mean? It simply means that we place our mind on the navel and "sense" it.

Placing Fire below Earth, i.e. attaching the mind to the navel, causes *the generative process* to begin, i.e. the production of qi. One of the names given to the navel is "Qi Abode". This is why.

Again, the inner "truth" is that we are always connected to Tao via the "life stem", Ming Di. We just don't realize it. This is primarily because we don't feel it. The navel is asleep.

Wuji Qi Gong teaches us to wake the navel up and "open" this pathway facilitating *communication* with Tao, of which we are part.

In yogic parlance, this is referred to as *manipura awakening*. When the navel awakens, we awaken to Shiva...Tao.

Heaven

Qi Abode
(Navel)

Earth

### *Step 3: The Practice of Fire*

Maintaining all of the conditions set forth in the instructions for *Man United With Heaven and Earth,* AND *The Practice of Air*:

1. Place your attention on the navel – sense it with your mind. (You may wonder, do I need to focus on a specific part of the navel, the outside, the inside, the very center, etc?)

No, at first it is useful to think of it as a small spherical area, maybe the size of a plum. Try to sense this entire area all at once.

2. Each time we inhale and exhale, we hold the attention on the navel, not letting the mind wander. At first our goal is to hold the mind on the navel for a single breath, then 2, then 3, etc.

3. When the mind wanders, we bring it back to the navel. At first this happens often, possibly several times per breath. This is OK, just bring it back and try to keep it there, for just one more complete breath.

4. Our goal is to be able to hold the mind on the navel for the entire duration of the practice, i.e. 1, 2, 3, 5, 10, minutes, recognizing that it will wander off now and then. *Our focus is both gentle and firm.*

*Note: This is not about "pushing" energy or "qi" down in the body. It is simply about gently but firmly attaching your attention to the navel. This facilitates the generation of qi at the navel.* **As a rule, in this practice we never ever force the movement of qi in the body.**

*Discussion:* The practice of Fire presents numerous challenges. The first is being able to sense the navel. At first we may have no awareness of it at all. How are we to focus on it when we have no awareness of it?

The answer is that we must first cultivate an awareness. This is not unlike cultivating awareness of the tip of the tongue, the end of the nose, or the right big toe.

We have awareness of these areas of the body because we use them often. How often do we use the navel?

Awareness of the navel is built by exercising it. The more we exercise it, the stronger the awareness becomes.

If need be, place your finger in your navel and apply very gentle pressure or movement. Then with your eyes closed, pay attention to this sensation. In time, the awareness will grow dramatically.

In fact, it will grow so much that you will never be without an awareness of it, even when you're not trying! All it takes is practice...

The second challenge is the matter of the mind wandering. When we "touch" the navel with the mind, the mind tends to become excited and immediately wanders off, thinking about a thousand other things, like a butterfly in a flower garden.

This happens because placing the mind on the navel is very "stimulating". This stimulation is an early indication of the energetic potency of the practice.

It is important not to over-react to this challenge. It must be met with patience and equanimity. Stress or strain defeats our success and must be avoided.

In time, the mind will slow down and become much more "tempered" and regulated in its behavior. This is an outcome of Earth tempering Fire!

With practice, we will be able to tell when the mind is about to wander before it happens.

# ~ *Earth* ~

*The Practice of Earth* involves surrendering to gravity. When we do this correctly, we can literally feel the body and Earth "communicating".

Earth exerts a clear downward pull, not just the outside of the body, but also the inside, every cell – the skin, the bones, the blood, and the qi.

So, the essential goal is to stand in *Man United With Heaven and Earth* and *let go to Earth*.

### *Step 4: The Practice Of Earth*

Maintaining all the conditions set forth in *Man United With Heaven and Earth,* AND *The Practice of Air,* AND *The Practice of Fire:*

1. Inhale and exhale slowly and deeply.

2. As you exhale relax the face, the tongue and throat, the diaphragm, the hands, the perineum, and the feet, "*letting the muscles go from the bone*". Let go of the qi and the blood.

3. Develop the sense that we are freeing all the cells of the body to *experience* gravity, allowing Earth to settle down...sink down.

4. Be careful to maintain optimal posture.

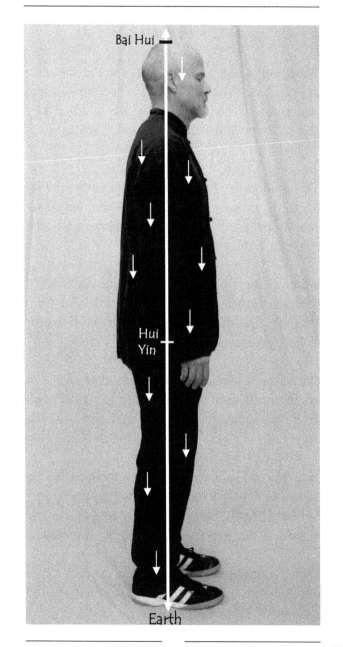

## ~ *Water* ~

Water is the second active agent in the alchemical process. When Water and Fire are brought into cautious proximity with one another they *react*, Water tempering Fire and Fire warming Water.

The product is steam – qi. The practice of Fire began the process of producing steam, but steam cannot be produced in any volume until the flame of Fire is robust.

Water is the final ingredient in the alchemical process. Hence, Water is the fourth and final step in establishing the necessary conditions for alchemy to occur.

Once we understand this step, then we can integrate all four steps into the practice, each time we practice, for the duration of the practice.

*The Practice of Water* is perhaps the most subtle and difficult part of the method. It can only be preformed correctly, once we have progressed to some degree in the previous three stages of practice.

This is because what we are actually raising is essence, "jin", and jin is formed via the alchemical process.

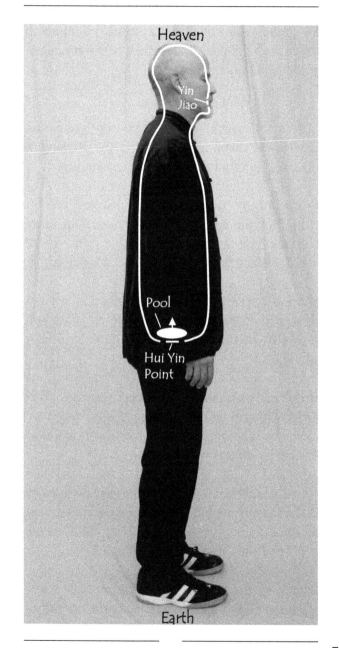

So it takes a short while for jin to accumulate to a significant degree. Jin forms when qi produced at the navel condenses into a pool at the base of the torso.

This pool resides just above the perineum, the lowest diaphragm in the body. Raising it involves flexing the perineum *very* slightly.

When done correctly, there is a distinct "heightening" of the sensation of the navel. In other words, while we are attaching the mind to the navel, raising Water "amplifies" the sensation.

We may also feel it as a heightening of the sensation of the hands, and if we pay attention carefully, of the whole body. Again, it is very subtle.

Jin is heavy like water or mercury. When we flex the diaphragm we feel it rise slightly. When we relax the diaphragm, we feel it lower again, as though by its own weight.

Note that this flexing can also be felt very clearly in the legs. In fact, if we flex the perineum very hard it effectively paralyzes the legs and we are unable to walk until we relax it again.

(If you try this, afterwards be sure to take a few minutes to consciously relax the perineum fully.)

Flexing the perineum has a very powerful neurological affect. This is one reason why we must be very careful how we manipulate this area of the body.

To effect Water optimally, we raise it *with as little effort as possible* until the sensation at the navel is maximized.

It is very subtle. Use as little effort as possible while achieving the desired effect. *Here the "middle way" is critically important. Too little and it fails to function, too much and things go wrong.*

*The Practice of Water* brings into play the Ren and Du meridians. These are special channels that rise up the front and back of the body, respectively. While they are thought to function productively in the young, as we age they become dormant.

Whether they become dormant as we age or whether we age because they become dormant is a question of interest.

In any case, *The Practice of Water* wakes them up and they begin to function to restore youthful vigor and vitality.

## Step 5: The Practice of Water

*Water must be raised very gently and without force. Raising it forcefully can result in undesirable neurological phenomena. Please heed this and all instructions.*

Maintaining all of the conditions set forth in the instructions for *Man United With Heaven And Earth*, AND T*he Practice of Air*, AND *The Practice of Fire*, AND *The Practice of Earth*:

1. With practice, the "pool" at the base of the torso "fills". As it fills, it becomes apparent, as though it possesses "weight", again like water or mercury. This happens over the course of several weeks or possibly months.

If "the pool" is not apparent, then there is nothing to "raise" and there is no need to engage in the practice of Raising Water. If so, just continue practicing the first three steps.

If Water is apparent, then we can continue.

2. When we lower Heaven to Fan Fire, we bring the breath down, down, down, to the Qi Hai. As we do so, we will notice a very slight tensing of muscles all over the body, this is natural.

3. One of the muscle groups that will begin

tensing is the perineum. As it tenses it will "lift" very slightly of its own accord – without conscious lifting on our part.

4. As we exhale, letting go inside, it along with all of the low threshold muscle motor units (very sensitive muscle fibers) of the body, relax. Consequently, if we pay attention, the perineum will relax and "fall" back to a relaxed position, as though the weight of the Water is doing the work. *This action is extremely subtle.*

5. The perineum rises very slightly as we inhale, and it relaxes again as we exhale. Practice this for a short time. It is very important that the perineum be able to relax and not become stuck in the flexed position.

(Because most of us carry tension in this area of the body all the time, the perineum is always flexed. To proceed, we *must* cultivate the ability to relax it. If we have worked with The Practice of Air, and incorporated slower, deeper, more rhythmic breathing into our daily lives, then the whole body, along with the perineum, will tend to relax more freely.)

6. Once we've developed the ability to relax the perineum at will, inhale down to the Qi Hai and feel how much the perineum flexes. Try to gauge the degree very carefully with your mind.

You may need to close your eyes to feel it.

Try it a few times, until you have a good feeling for the degree, as this is the precise degree to which we desire to hold it lifted.

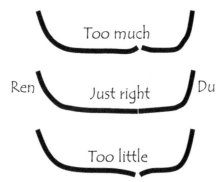

Ren and Du Channels and Proper Flexion

In other words, once we establish the precise degree of flexion, we will consciously hold this flexion even when we exhale.

The ideal flexion is depicted in the diagram. Too little and Ren and Du channels to not align. Too much and again they do not align. When perineum flexion is just right, they align perfectly, the "circuit" being completed.

The "effort" required is like that needed to lift a single sheet of paper. It is more the intent to lift than the actual lifting that we are looking for. When we get it just right we will feel it throughout the entire body, like electricity flowing. The feeling can be very intense, like a surging of blood and electricity running through the body with each breath.

Once you feel it, continue to explore it, attempting to integrate it fully into your practice session. Try it for 1, 2, 3, 5, 10, minutes.

***When we're not formally practicing, we allow the perineum to relax. Please heed this and all instructions.***

## *Discussion:*

Raising Water has the effect of *perfectly* connecting Ren and Du meridians. The Ren meridian (conception vessel) begins at the very bottom of the torso (Hui Yin point) and rises up the front of the body, ending inside the lower lip at Cheng Jiang (Sauce Receptacle), Ren 24.

The Du meridian (governing vessel) begins at a point just beneath the tail bone Chang Qiang (Long Strong, a.k.a. Stairway To Heaven) and rises up the back and over the head ending at a point behind the upper lip at Gum Intersection (Du 28).

When we lift the perineum "just so", a "connection" is established between Hui Yin and Chang Qiang, connecting Ren and Du meridians.

When we touched the tongue to Gum Intersection (Du 28) as we did in step 5 of *Man United With Heaven And Earth*, we connected the upper ends of the Ren and Du meridians. With upper and lower ends connected, Ren and Du meridians function as a "loop". (This loop is often referred to as the micro-cosmic obit.)

This being so, we will not concern ourselves with it. Focusing on it is a mistake.

In time, it will take care of itself. All we have to do is continue to practice what we've learned *– that's all*.

Once understood the practice is simple, but not easy. There is a tendency to complicate these instructions with physical or mental machinations.

This urge arises in an attempt to escape the requirement for prolonged attention. Instead, stay focused and try to avoid this impulse.

A last point regarding the accumulation of jin, the pool at the base of the torso...

Orgasm expends this energy. To experience this accumulation, and certainly to progress in the practice, it is necessary to be judicious in this regard. *Water must be conserved.*

# ~ Wuji Qi Gong - The Experience ~

What is it like? What can we expect?

The very first thing we can expect to feel is that as we go about life, we stand taller and are more vertically centered and balanced. With this comes a natural sense of increased energy and vitality.

We may notice an increase in strength, particularly strength that involves vertical actions of the body.

This vertical centered-ness and strength are the "zhong ding" or "central stability" of Taijiquan, Baguazhang, and other traditional Chinese martial arts. (Taijiquan is *"great aspiring to Heaven fist"*.)

There is a gradual increase in peripheral awareness and reflexes. If we open a cabinet and something falls, we catch it instinctively.

With the adoption of slow deep breathing and the accumulation of Yin comes a natural letting go, and with this, increased comfort, flexibility, and freedom of movement.

We begin to feel the breath move throughout the body with each inhalation and exhalation.

The *dan tien* and *the jingluo (meridians)* become apparent. Joints "open" allowing blood and energy to flow freely throughout the body, nourishing flesh, tendon, bone.

With each exhalation blood bathes the abdomen (the Qi Hai) and the brain. With each inhalation blood returns to the heart and lungs to be renewed.

The mind comes under our conscious control. Mental chatter ceases. (This is a function of placing Fire below Earth!) When we relax the mind, it returns to a state of "no thought".

When we breathe while we labor, work "gets done". "It" does it. This is what Lao Tzu means by "doing little, yet accomplishing everything". This is a quintessential Zen experience.

As our awareness of the vertical center line (the Chong meridian) grows, all of the "chakras" become apparent and continue to grow in prominence.

The *celestial stems* emerge from their respective centers. While this meaning is all but lost today, these are the principal energetic pathways by which we are connected to Tao. In Hindi, they are the "dvadashanta" or "12 ends", connecting us to Shiva.

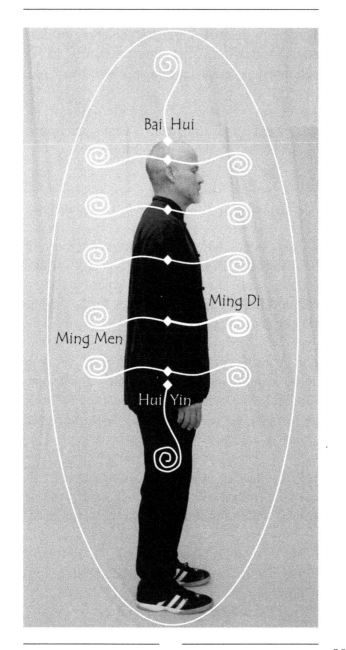

Bai Hui

Ming Di

Ming Men

Hui Yin

There is a distinct sense that the energy in the body is growing, expanding outwardly like a balloon. It is believed that this is in fact true.

As the energy expands beyond the limits of our skin, there is a distinct change in the perception of our body boundary – it dissolves.

We no longer feel as though we are squeezed into a package, confined within an envelope.

This is a very gradual process that is not the least bit disturbing. However, in retrospect it is quite peculiar – we lose the sense of where we begin and end. This *diffusion* continues for as long as we continue to practice.

This specific perception is believed to be a quintessential experience of the Taoist pursuit and one that underpins much of Taoist philosophy, i.e. *as we continue the practice, we dissolve into Tao.*

We find that our mind or "Yi", is no longer limited to the confines of the body, but is free to move around within the limits of our energetic reach.

Fears dissolve. We're left with a *powerful* sense of calm, equanimity, and understanding.

*This is the practice of Wuji Qi Gong.*

*~Appendix~*

# Hexagrams of The Elemental Process

| Gua | Hexagram | Combined | Character | Pin Yin | Meaning | Number |
|---|---|---|---|---|---|---|
| Heaven / Fire | | Heaven Over Fire | 同人 | Tong Ren | The same purpose | 13 |
| Fire / Earth | | Fire Over Earth | 晉 | Jin | Advance | 35 |
| Earth / Water | | Earth Over Water | 師 | Shi | Collective force | 7 |
| Water / Heaven | | Water Over Heaven | 需 | Xu | Measured waiting | 5 |
| **The Inner Hexagrams** | | | | | | |
| Heaven / Wind | | Heaven Over Wind | 姤 | Gou | Joining | 44 |
| Water / Mountain | | Water Over Mountain | 蹇 | Jian | Uneven, limping | 39 |
| Earth / Thunder | | Earth Over Thunder | 復 | Fu | Returning, reborn | 24 |
| Fire / Lake | | Fire Over Lake | 睽 | Kui | Separation | 38 |

The top gua of the "inner" hexagram is derived by joining the bottom two lines from the top gua and the top line from the bottom gua of the original hexagram. Similarly, the bottom gua is derived by joining the bottom line from the top gua and the top two lines of the bottom gua.

# Hexagrams of The Alchemical Process

| Gua | Hexagram | Combined | Character | Pin Yin | Meaning | Number |
|---|---|---|---|---|---|---|
| Heaven / Water | | Heaven Over Water | 訟 | Song | Resolution of conflict, attainment of peace | 6 |
| Water / Earth | | Water Over Earth | 比 | Bi | Union | 8 |
| Earth / Fire | | Earth Over Fire | 明夷 | Ming Yi | Clarity, insight | 36 |
| Fire / Heaven | | Fire Over Heaven | 大有 | Da You | Great possession | 14 |
| **The Inner Hexagrams** | | | | | | |
| Wind / Fire | | Wind Over Fire | 家人 | Jia ren | The clan | 37 |
| Mountain / Earth | | Mountain Over Earth | 剝 | Bo | Peel away the false to explore the truth | 23 |
| Thunder / Water | | Thunder Over Water | 解 | Xie | Liberation | 40 |
| Lake / Heaven | | Lake Over Heaven | 夬 | Guai | Resolution for the good | 43 |

# *Samkhyan Model of Manifestation And Its Reverse - The Yogic Process, Circa 3500 B.C.E.*

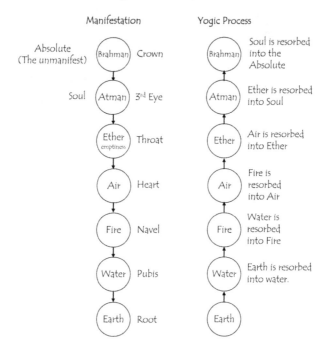

The Samkhyan model of manifestation describes the process by which matter and consciousness precipitate from the Absolute, the heavier from the lighter, the gross from the subtle.

The yogic model describes the process of demanifestation by which matter and consciousness return to the Absolute, the heavier being resorbed into the lighter, the gross into the subtle.

## *The Samkhyan Model Evolves Into A Cross*

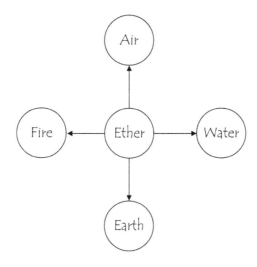

Referring to the **Rasarnava**, "He (Bhairava) begins his discussion by speaking of the fifth element, space or ether which is called the fifth "house". This he distinguishes from the four other houses, which are "placed in front"; that is, they are arranged like the arms of a cross, with the empty fifth house standing as a central court-yard."[13] Bhairava is a manifestation of Shiva.

In this configuration we see the elements in opposition as we see them in the Bagua, Ether, the unseen essence of the universe occupying the center.

## *Etymology of The Character for "Navel"*

The ancient character "pi": "navel".

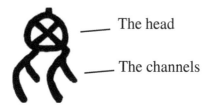 — The head

— The channels

From *Chinese Characters* - Pi: "the navel which is supposed to be in communication with the head through channels in which circulate the - 氣 vital spirits."[5]

Pi (the modern character): "adjoin".

 "Adjoin" referring to the point of adjoinment, i.e. the navel, but no longer meaning navel. The upper portion no longer means "head". In this evolution its original meaning is all but lost.[12]

The modern character for navel: "duqi".

## *Etymology of The Character "Ji"*

Ji: Extreme limit, zenith.

This character is used in several hundred combinations almost all connoting: a) extreme limit, b) pole. It implies a constant reaching upward intention, i.e. "aspiring to Heaven". This reaching accentuates a vertical line in the body, much like the tree. This line is the Chong meridian.

Xiu: worn out

Tree reaching toward Heaven, rooted in Earth

Heaven

Mouth

Hands

Earth

Ji: "A man who acts, who struggles, with his mouth and with his hand, between Heaven and Earth, to gain his *point*".[11]

Obstacle

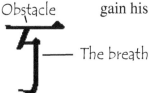

The breath

Qiao: The breath struggling against an obstacle to connect with Heaven

# ~ *Notes* ~

1. Reprinted from *The Secret of Everlasting Life*, Bertschinger, R., p. 112, with permission of the author. (p. 10)

2. Reprinted from *The Secret of Everlasting Life*, Bertschinger, R., p. 166, with permission of the author. (p. 22)

3. Reprinted from *The Yellow Emperor's Classic of Internal Chinese Medicine*, Veith, I., p. 17, with permission from University of California Press. (p. 35)

4. Reprinted from *The Secret of The Golden Flower*, translation by Cleary, T., p. 11, with permission Harper Collins Publications. (p. 48)

5. Reprinted from *Chinese Characters*, Weiger, L., p. 81, Paragon Book Reprint Corp. and Dover Publications, Inc., 1927, with permission Dover Publications. (p. 51)

6. Reprinted from *Chinese Characters*, Weiger, L., p. 28, Paragon Book Reprint Corp. and Dover Publications, Inc., 1927, with permission Dover Publications. (p. 53)

7. Reprinted from *The Secret of The Golden Flower*, translation by Cleary, T., p. 26, with permisson of Harper Collins Publications. (p. 53)

8. Reprinted from *The Yellow Emperor's Classic of Internal Chinese Medicine*, Veith, I., p. 105, with permission from University of California Press. (p. 58)

9. Reprinted from *The Secret of Everlasting Life*, Bertschinger, R., p. 158, with permission of the author. (p. 58)

10. *The Secret of The Golden Flower*, translation by Cleary, T., p. 11, Harper Collins, 1991. (p. 63)

11. Reprinted from *Chinese Characters*, Weiger, L., p. 28, Paragon Book Reprint Corp. and Dover Publications, Inc., 1927, with permission Dover Publicatons. (p. 53)

12. *Chinese Characters*, Weiger, L., p. 81, Paragon Book Reprint Corp. and Dover Publications, Inc., 1927. (p. 96)

13. Reprinted from *The Alchemical Body*, White, D., p. 180, with permission of University of Chicago Press, 1996, (p. 95).

## ~ *References* ~

1. Bertschinger, R., *The Secret of Everlasting Life*, Element, 1994.

2. Blok, F., *The I Ching, Landscapes of the Soul*, Blozo Products, Amsterdam, 2000.

3. Cleary, T., translation, *The Inner Teachings of Taoism*, Shambala, 1986.

4. Cleary, T., *The Secret of The Golden Flower*, Harper Collins, New York, 1991.

5. Elliott, S., Edmonson, D., *Coherent Breathing - The Definitive Method*, Coherence Press, 2008.

6. Elliott, S., Edmonson, D., *The New Science of Breath*, Coherence Press, 2005.

7. Ellis, A., Wiseman, N., Boss, K., *Grasping The Wind*, Paradigm Publications, 1989.

8. Henricks, R. translation, *Lao-Tzu Te-Tao Ching*, Ballantine Books, 1989.

9. Jaideva Singh, *Siva Sutras - The Yoga of Sumpreme Identity*, Motilal Banarsidass, 1979.

10. Liao, Waysun, *T'ai Chi Classics*, Shambala, 1977.

11. Lu, Kuan-Yu, *Taoist Yoga, Alchemy & Immortality*, Samuel Weiser, 1973.

12. May Ke., *Book Of The Ceremony (From Entry To Expert One-Pass)*, Guangxi Publishing House, 2008.

13. Men Den, translation, *Wujishi Breathing Exercise*, Medicine and Health Publishing Company, Hong Kong, 1994.

14. Painter, J., *Combat Baguazhang: Nine Dragon System, Volume One, Forms and Principles*, Unique Publications, 2007.

15. Ren, Fa-Rong, *Zhou Yi Can Tong Qi Shi Yi*, Northwest University Publishing.

16. Veith, I., *The Yellow Emperor's Classic of Internal Chinese Medicine*, University of California Press, 1949.

17. Wilhelm, R., Baynes, C., translation, *The I Ching*, The Bollingen Foundation, 1950.

18. White, D., *The Alchemical Body*, University of Chicago Press, 1996.

19. Wieger, L., *Chinese Characters*, Dover Publications, 1927.

20. Wong, E., *Cultivating Stillness*, Shambala, 1992.

# ~ General ~

*~ Man United With Heaven & Earth ~*

*~ The Practice of Air ~*

## ~ *The Practice of Fire* ~

*~ The Practice of Earth ~*

107

## ~ *The Practice Of Water* ~

KO2646 38230  Doller
800 774 2354
      42
Dollar 408 999 6561
      858 621 4109
Ashley

9 780978 639945